GRAPHIC LIBRARY™

GRAPHIC EXPEDITIONS

BUILDING THE GREAT WALL OF CHINA

AN *Isabel Soto*
HISTORY ADVENTURE

Terry Collins

illustrated by Joe Staton and Al Milgrom

Raintree

www.raintreepublishers.co.uk
Visit our website to find out
more information about
Raintree books.

To order:
☎ Phone 0845 6044371
🖨 Fax +44 (0) 1865 312263
✉ Email myorders@raintreepublishers.co.uk

Customers from outside the UK please telephone +44 1865 312262

Raintree is an imprint of Capstone Global Library Limited, a company incorporated in England
and Wales having its registered office at 7 Pilgrim Street, London EC4V 6LB
Registered company number: 6695882

Text © Capstone Press 2010
First published by Capstone Press in 2010
First published in hardback in the United Kingdom by Capstone Global Library Ltd in 2011
The moral rights of the proprietor have been asserted.

British Library Cataloguing in Publication Data
Collins, Terry – Building the Great Wall of China: an Isabel Soto history investigation
A full catalogue record for this book is available from the British Library.

ISBN 978 1 406 22588 4 (hardback)
15 14 13 12 11
10 9 8 7 6 5 4 3 2 1

Designer: Alison Thiele
Cover artists: Tod Smith
Colourist: Krista Ward
Media researcher: Wanda Winch
Editors: Christopher Harbo and Diyan Leake
Originated by Capstone Global Library Ltd
Printed and bound in China by South China Printing Company Limited

Photo Credits: AP ... ...ekrasov, 13

Design Elements: S... ...gn); mmmm (world map
design); Mushakesa (abstract lines design); Najin (old parchment design)

CONTENTS

Chisholm Trail, Texas, 1876

My grandfather used to say, "Isabel, people can learn a great deal from history."

I've been studying cattle drives for two days now. All I've learned is how it feels to be soaking wet.

I wish something interesting would happen.

BOOM!

STAMPEDE!

My grandfather also used to say, "Be careful what you wish for. It just might come true."

The Tumu Crisis of 1449 began when Zhu Qizhen was the sixth emperor of China's Ming Dynasty.

Tired of being invaded by Mongolia, he led his soldiers into a great battle.

However, the fight ended when the Mongols captured the emperor.

Meanwhile, Zhu Qizhen's brother Zhu Qiyu was named as the new emperor.

But with the Chinese Army defeated, how would China fight back?

THE MING DYNASTY

The Ming Dynasty began ruling China in 1368. The dynasty was founded when the Han Chinese overthrew the Yuan Dynasty. The Ming Dynasty's government lasted 276 years. During that time, Chinese literature, art, and philosophy grew. The dynasty came to an end in 1644 when the Qing Dynasty rose to power.

Zhu Qiyu's advisors recommended another kind of protection. For centuries, the Chinese had used walls to protect their cities and lands.

These primitive walls were old and worn.

They were incomplete and spread out across the northern Chinese border.

But a new "great" wall made of brick and stone could keep out the Mongol raiders.

This wall would be longer, taller, and stronger.

We're on the Badaling. This part of the wall was built during the Ming Dynasty.

That's fascinating, Dad. ⇒yawn⇐

During that time, more than 1 million soldiers guarded the Great Wall.

Were they all as bored as I am?

Think about it, Eddie. The Great Wall is so big, astronauts could see it from the Moon.

Actually, that's a myth. The wall is large, but it can't be seen from the Moon with the naked eye.

OTHER GREAT WALL MYTHS

Myth: The bodies of builders are buried inside the Great Wall.

Truth: Historians believe angry Chinese peasants started this myth because they were forced to work on the wall.

Myth: The Great Wall is one long wall with no breaks.

Truth: The wall stops and starts in several places.

What brings you to China, Dr Soto?

Would you believe it had something to do with a cattle stampede?

Eddie? Now where has that boy gone?

Uh-oh. I've got a pretty good idea.

CHECK THE MAP

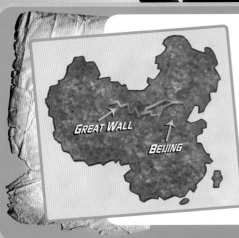

GREAT WALL

BEIJING

The Great Wall of China is the longest structure on Earth made by humans. It has several different sections. Depending on what part of China is visited, the wall may be either unbroken or in ruins. Vandals have damaged many parts of the wall. Other parts of the wall have been knocked down for new construction projects. People have even stolen bricks to build their own homes.

Great Wall of China, 221 BC

What did I say about not touching the other buttons?

Sorry, Dr Soto. But you've got to check this out.

I had no idea the Great Wall started this way.

This is the era of Emperor Shi Huangdi. He decided to build a wall to keep raiders out of his empire. His wall linked sections of other walls built long before he became emperor.

It would be a new wall. A mighty wall. A Great Wall.

THE FIRST ROYAL EMPEROR OF CHINA

Emperor Shi Huangdi founded the Qin Dynasty and brought China together. Roads were built to connect the cities. A central government was put in place. The Chinese now used the same money, measures, and written language.

The emperor used forced labour to build the Great Wall.

Some labourers were criminals, but most were peasants. The poor had no choice but to obey their leader.

Dr Soto, this wall looks different from the one back in our time.

That's because the first wall was built with soil and stones.

Bamboo poles were tied together and used to hold the soil and stones. Then workers used stone tools to pound the earth in place.

Each part of the wall was built in layers. When a section was tall enough, the bamboo frames were moved to start the next piece.

17

Stick close. I'll open another portal. I'm taking you back to your parents.

Come on. Let's jump!

Great Wall of China, 1642

Are we there yet?

No. The WISP says we've arrived around the end of the Ming Dynasty.

So put in the right date, and let's try again.

It's not that simple. Something must be wrong with the WISP. I hope it's not damaged.

Hold on, soldiers are coming.

Great Wall of China, present day

We made it!

THUMP!

Edward James Elliot! Your mother and I were worried sick!

I knew he would be safe with Dr Soto watching him.

What's with the headgear?

Are you all right, son?

Souvenir.

I'm fine, but the Great Wall of China is awesome!

26

I never thought Eddie would be so excited about history. Thank you, Dr Soto.

First-hand knowledge is what hooked him, not me.

Eddie just needed to see with his own eyes what went into the building of the Great Wall.

I think we can all be glad that one of the world's most amazing building achievements is still standing.

Enjoy the rest of your stay in China, Eddie.

Don't worry, Dr Soto. I will!

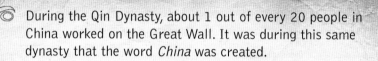

During the Qin Dynasty, about 1 out of every 20 people in China worked on the Great Wall. It was during this same dynasty that the word *China* was created.

Building the Great Wall was very expensive. To pay for the materials, the Chinese government increased poor people's taxes. These taxes caused many citizens to dislike the wall.

The average height of the Great Wall is 8 metres (25 feet). The width of the wall ranges from 5 to 8 metres (15 to 25 feet). Along most sections, a roadway 4 metres (13 feet) wide runs along the top of the wall.

The Great Wall was built to defend China from raiders and other invaders. Today the wall serves as a popular tourist destination. Each year, more than 10 million tourists visit the Great Wall.

The Badaling is one of the most visited sections of the Great Wall. This section was built during the Ming Dynasty. It is located about 69 kilometres (43 miles) north of China's capital of Beijing. The Badaling section is famous for the way the Great Wall snakes up and down mountain slopes.

On 25 June 1899, a hoax appeared in newspapers across the United States. In this fake story, rumours flew about American businessmen planning to tear down the Great Wall. They would then build a road in its place to help the Chinese economy.

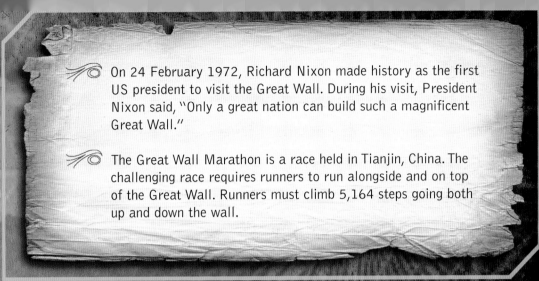

On 24 February 1972, Richard Nixon made history as the first US president to visit the Great Wall. During his visit, President Nixon said, "Only a great nation can build such a magnificent Great Wall."

The Great Wall Marathon is a race held in Tianjin, China. The challenging race requires runners to run alongside and on top of the Great Wall. Runners must climb 5,164 steps going both up and down the wall.

MORE ABOUT

Isabel Soto

NAME: Isabel "Izzy" Soto
INTERESTS: People and places
BUILD: Athletic   **HAIR:** Dark Brown
EYES: Brown   **HEIGHT:** 1.70 m

WISP: The Worldwide Inter-dimensional Space/Time Portal developed by Max Axiom at Axiom Laboratory.

BACKSTORY: Isabel "Izzy" Soto caught the humanities bug as a little girl. Every night, her grandfather told her about his adventures exploring ancient ruins in South America. He believed people can learn a lot from other cultures and places.

Izzy's interest in cultures followed her through school and beyond. She studied history and geography. On one research trip, she discovered an ancient stone with mysterious energy. Izzy took the stone to Super Scientist Max Axiom, who determined that the stone's energy cuts across space and time. Harnessing the power of the stone, he built a device called the WISP. It opens windows to any place and any time. Although she must not use the WISP to change history, Izzy now explores events wherever and whenever they happen, solving a few mysteries along the way.

GLOSSARY

achievement successful accomplishment, especially after a lot of effort

bamboo very tall tropical grass with a hard, hollow stem

catapult weapon used to hurl rocks, liquid, or other items at an enemy

crisis time of danger or difficulty

dynasty series of rulers belonging to the same family or group

emperor male ruler of an empire. Chinese emperors made all the decisions for the people they ruled.

enthusiasm great excitement or interest

myth false idea that many people believe

peasant poor person who owns a small farm or works on a farm, especially in Europe and some Asian countries

philosophy the study of truth, wisdom, the nature of reality, and knowledge

primitive relating to an early stage of development

sorcery magic that controls evil spirits

stampede when a group of animals makes a sudden, wild rush in one direction, usually because something has frightened them

FIND OUT MORE

Books

Ancient China (China Focus), Charlotte Guillain (Heinemann Library, 2008)

China (Countries in the News), Iris Teichmann (Franklin Watts, 2009)

Welcome to China, Caryn Jenner (Dorling Kindersley, 2008)

Internet sites

www.thebeijingguide.com/great_wall_of_china/index.html
Visit this website to take a virtual tour of the Great Wall of China.

china.mrdonn.org
You can find lots of information about ancient China on this website. There is also a link to a page on the Great Wall.

www.britishmuseum.org/explore/young_explorers1.aspx
This British Museum website has lots of games to play that will help you explore the ancient world.